Best of
BIDEN

"Don't judge a book by its cover"

ISBN: 978-1-955622-64-6

For more information contact:

bestofbiden@gmail.com

PRINTED IN THE UNITED STATES

CPSIA information can be obtained
at www.ICGtesting.com
Printed in the USA
FSHW011202100222
88210FS